THIS JOURNAL BELONGS TO...

ℒℯ𝓉'𝓈 𝒞ℰℒℰℬℛ𝒜𝒯ℰ!

A lot can happen in 100 days. You can be inspired to begin
something new and learn to appreciate what you have in new
ways. And it doesn't have to be difficult. Just write, doodle, and
color you way to fresh, Christ-centered insights and perspectives!

Start at the beginning, middle or end…it only matters that you start.
So have fun and allow God to lead you every step of the way.

…And who knows but that you have come to your royal
position for such a time as this? — ESTHER 4:14

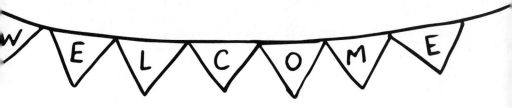

What I hope to gain from this book...

_____

_____

_____

_____

_____

_____

_____

_____

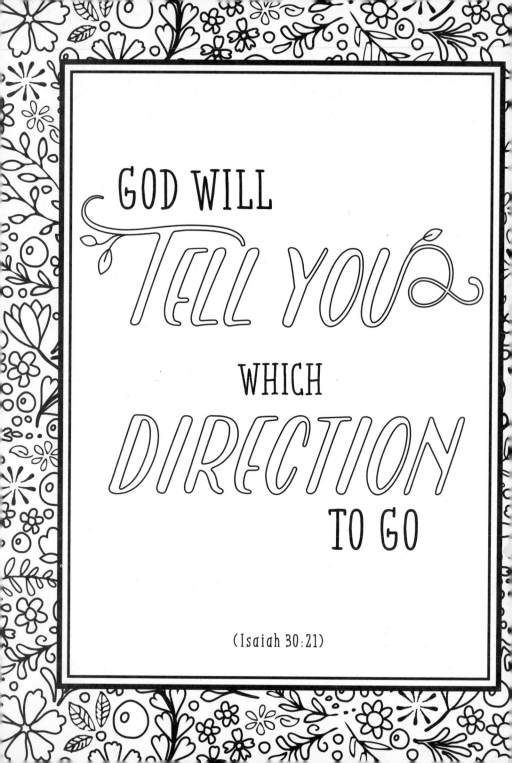

The first time God spoke to me...

Do not be anxious about anything, but in every situation, by prayer and petition, with thanksgiving, present your requests to God. And the peace of God, which transcends all understanding, will guard your hearts and your minds in Christ Jesus. — PHILIPPIANS 4:6-7

FUN THINGS TO DO WHEN I HAVE TIME FOR MYSELF...

"God wants to speak to you on a One-to-one basis, every day."

– JOYCE

What distractions should you limit or remove from your life in order to hear more clearly from God?

DRAW A TURNING POINT IN YOUR LIFE

But the Comforter (Counselor, Helper, Intercessor, Advocate, Strengthener, Standby), the Holy Spirit, Whom the Father will send in My name [in My place, to represent Me and act on My behalf], He will teach you all things. And He will cause you to recall (will remind you of, bring to your remembrance) everything I have told you. — JOHN 14:26

Quiet down. Be still. Listen. What is God telling you?

ILLUSTRATE YOUR
FAVORITE SCRIPTURE

"God knew we would need help in understanding His plan for us, so He sent the Holy Spirit to dwell on the inside of every Christian. He is our Guide, our Teacher of truth, our Counselor, and our Helper."

— JOYCE

The "silver lining" of the last challenge God helped me through was...

_____

_____

_____

_____

_____

_____

_____

_____

_____

_____

_____

_____

_____

_____

_____

_____

_____

_____

_____

_____

_____

May he give you the desire of your heart and make all your plans succeed. — PSALM 20:4

PICKING FLOWERS

Add flowers to this empty vase.

I will instruct you and teach you in the way you should go; I will
counsel you with my loving eye on you. — PSALM 32:8

TIME TO GROW MORE FLOWERS...

Use this space to draw some more flowers.

GOD DIRECTS OUR STEPS

We make our plans for the future, but the Lord
directs our steps and makes them sure. (Proverbs 16:9)

1 Write down all your plans for this season.

_____

_____

_____

_____

_____

_____

_____

_____

_____

_____

_____

_____

_____

_____

_____

_____

_____

_____

_____

_____

_____

_____

_____

_____

_____

_____

_____

_____

_____

_____

_____

_____

_____

_____

_____

_____

_____

_____

_____

_____

_____

_____

_____

_____

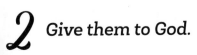 *2* Give them to God.

3 Check back at a later date to see if God's plans were better than yours.

4 Write what you discovered.

_____

_____

_____

_____

_____

_____

_____

_____

_____

_____

_____

_____

_____

_____

_____

_____

_____

_____

_____

_____

_____

The steps of a [good] man are directed and established by the Lord when He delights in his way [and He busies Himself with his every step]. Though he falls, he shall not be utterly cast down, for the Lord grasps his hand in support and upholds him. — PSALM 37:23-24

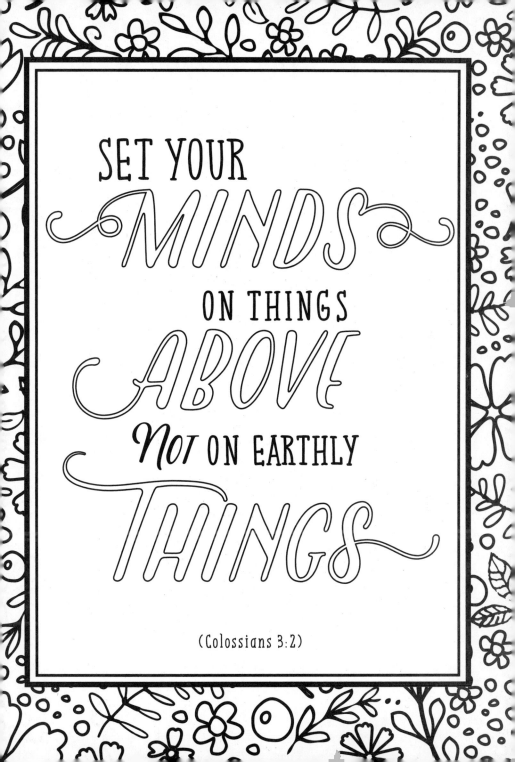

SET YOUR
MINDS
ON THINGS
ABOVE
Not ON EARTHLY
THINGS

(Colossians 3:2)

A REVERSE BUCKET LIST

List some of the things you are proud to have accomplished.

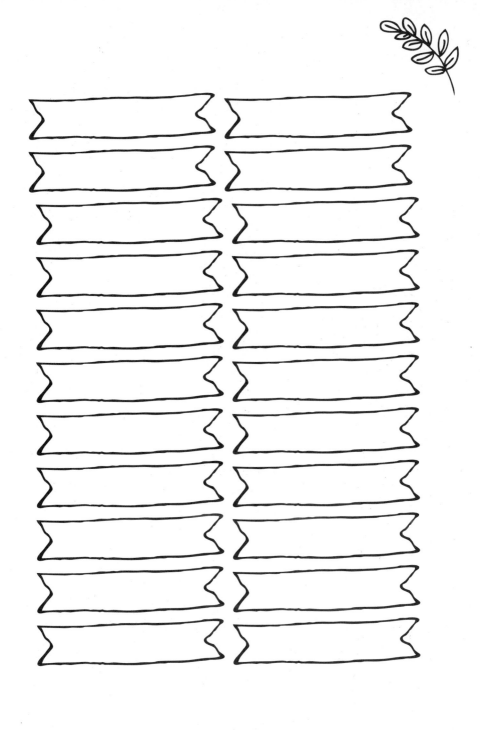

THIS SPACE IS DEDICATED TO INTERNAL MONOLOGUE

"You can have
a great life,
but you have
to think the
way God tells
you to think."

— JOYCE

What's awesome about you? List your BEST qualities.

You are my hiding place; You will protect me from trouble and surround me with songs of deliverance. — PSALM 32:7

For who has known or understood the mind (the counsels and purposes) of the Lord so as to guide and instruct Him and give Him knowledge? But we have the mind of Christ (the Messiah) and do hold the thoughts (feelings and purposes) of His heart. — 1 CORINTHIANS 2:16

How have you changed since you began your relationship with Jesus?

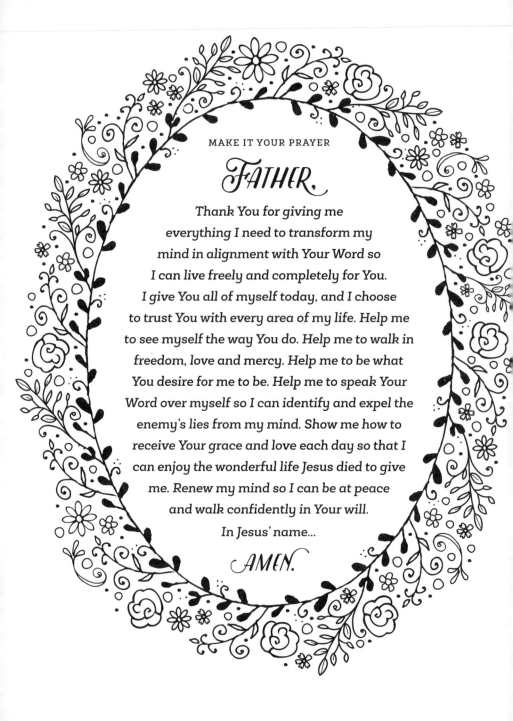

MAKE IT YOUR PRAYER

Father,

Thank You for giving me
everything I need to transform my
mind in alignment with Your Word so
I can live freely and completely for You.
I give You all of myself today, and I choose
to trust You with every area of my life. Help me
to see myself the way You do. Help me to walk in
freedom, love and mercy. Help me to be what
You desire for me to be. Help me to speak Your
Word over myself so I can identify and expel the
enemy's lies from my mind. Show me how to
receive Your grace and love each day so that I
can enjoy the wonderful life Jesus died to give
me. Renew my mind so I can be at peace
and walk confidently in Your will.

In Jesus' name...

Amen.

JUST DOODLE...

"You're okay, and you're on your way!"

[Inasmuch as we] refute arguments and theories and reasonings and every proud and lofty thing that sets itself up against the [true] knowledge of God; and we lead every thought and purpose away captive into the obedience of Christ (the Messiah, the Anointed One). — 2 CORINTHIANS 10:5

Think about the last experience that stressed you out. If it happens again, how will you respond differently, with God's help?

How many ways can you
DRAW A HEART?

Or draw anything that reminds you of love.

And let the peace (soul harmony which comes) from Christ rule (act as umpire continually) in your hearts [deciding and settling with finality all questions that arise in your minds, in that peaceful state] to which as [members of Christ's] one body you were also called [to live]. And be thankful (appreciative), [giving praise to God always]. — COLOSSIANS 3:15

DECLUTTER & SIMPLIFY

List the clutter you will eliminate from your life this year:

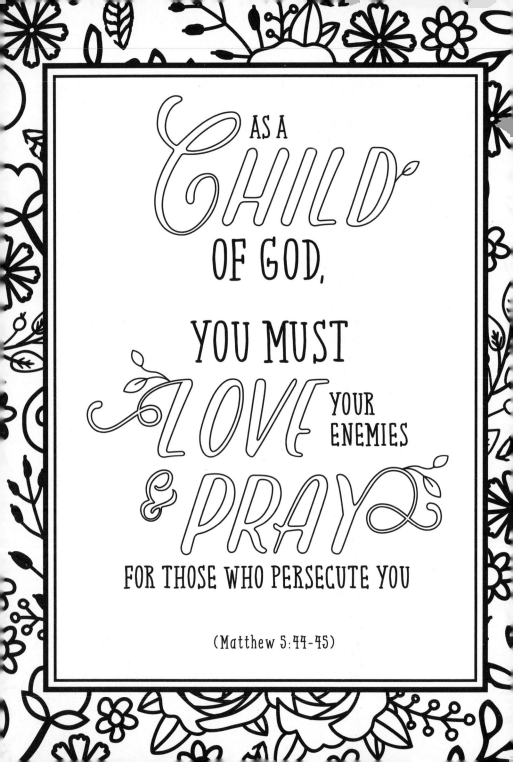

AS A
CHILD
OF GOD,
YOU MUST
LOVE YOUR ENEMIES
& PRAY
FOR THOSE WHO PERSECUTE YOU

(Matthew 5:44-45)

DRAW YOUR FAVORITE MEMORY

Life is too short to hold a grudge. Do you have unfinished business with someone? Are you ready to get past it?

But if you do not forgive others their trespasses [their reckless and willful sins, leaving them, letting them go, and giving up resentment], neither will your Father forgive you your trespasses.

— MATTHEW 6:15

Only use your favorite color on this page

"Once you see how damaging unforgiveness is to your life, it will motivate you to do all you can to live free from it."

— JOYCE

LET IT GO

I am ready to forgive... _____

_____

_____

For doing this... _____

_____

_____

_____

_____

_____

_____

_____

_____

_____

_____

_____

_____

_____

_____

_____

_____

_____

It made me feel... _____

_____

_____

_____

_____

_____

_____

_____

_____

_____

_____

_____

_____

_____

_____

_____

_____

_____

_____

_____

For we know Him Who said, Vengeance is Mine [retribution and the meting out of full justice rest with Me]; I will repay [I will exact the compensation], says the Lord. And again, The Lord will judge and determine and solve and settle the cause and the cases of His people. — HEBREWS 10:30

Let it Go

(one more time)

I am ready to forgive... _____

_____

_____

For doing this... _____

_____

_____

_____

_____

_____

_____

_____

_____

_____

_____

_____

_____

_____

_____

_____

It made me feel... _____

_____

_____

_____

_____

_____

_____

_____

_____

_____

_____

_____

_____

_____

_____

_____

_____

_____

_____

_____

_____

_____

_____

When angry, do not sin; do not ever let your wrath (your exasper-
ation, your fury or indignation) last until the sun goes down. Leave
no [such] room or foothold for the devil [give no opportunity to him].

— EPHESIANS 4:26-27

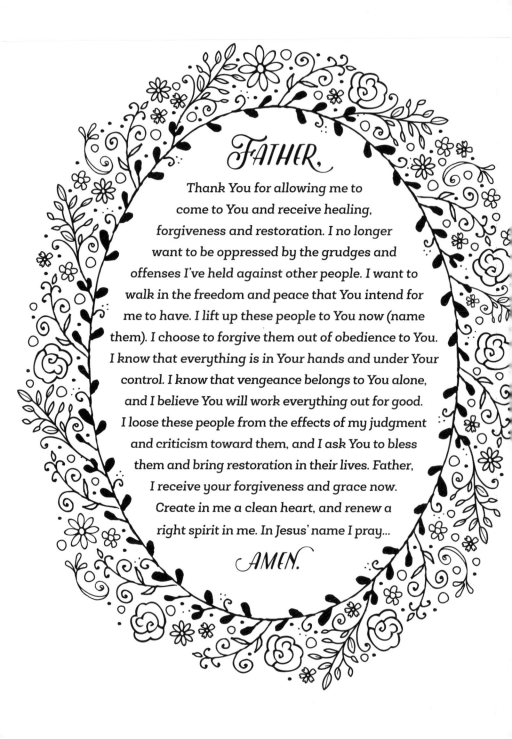

FATHER,

Thank You for allowing me to come to You and receive healing, forgiveness and restoration. I no longer want to be oppressed by the grudges and offenses I've held against other people. I want to walk in the freedom and peace that You intend for me to have. I lift up these people to You now (name them). I choose to forgive them out of obedience to You. I know that everything is in Your hands and under Your control. I know that vengeance belongs to You alone, and I believe You will work everything out for good. I loose these people from the effects of my judgment and criticism toward them, and I ask You to bless them and bring restoration in their lives. Father, I receive your forgiveness and grace now. Create in me a clean heart, and renew a right spirit in me. In Jesus' name I pray...

AMEN.

EXT STEPS...

If you prayed that prayer and meant it from
your heart, do these three simple steps:

- 1 -

Tear out your LET IT GO page.

- 2 -

Rip it up and throw it away, or safely burn it.

- 3 -

Now smile and take a deep breath...and exhale.
Be free in Christ, and never look back.

GOD'S WORD IS THE SWORD OF THE SPIRIT

What do you think that Sword of the Spirit would look like?
Draw a sword. (see Ephesians 6:17)

God's got your back. Write Him a letter and give Him all of your cares and worries.

"Forgiving others of their offense is much easier when we are truly aware of our own sins and shortcomings. God never asks us to do for another what He has not first done for us."

– JOYCE

Ask someone for

FORGIVENESS

DEAR _____,

If I could, I would turn back time and take back
what I said or did to hurt you. Please forgive
me for... _____

_____

_____

_____

_____

_____

_____

_____

_____

_____

_____

_____

_____

_____

_____

_____

_____

_____

_____

_____

_____

_____

_____

_____

_____

_____

_____

_____

_____

_____

_____

_____

_____

_____

_____

_____

_____

_____

_____

_____

_____

So repent (change your mind and purpose); turn around and return [to God], that your sins may be erased (blotted out, wiped clean), that times of refreshing (of recovering from the effects of heat, of reviving with fresh air) may come from the presence of the Lord.

— ACTS 3:19

_____

_____

_____

_____

_____

_____

_____

_____

_____

_____

_____

_____

_____

_____

_____

_____

_____

_____

_____

"Satan uses unforgiveness against people more than any other thing. He uses it to separate and divide, to weaken and destroy, and to hinder our fellowship with God. And these are only a few of the devastating effects of unforgiveness." - JOYCE

DRAW SOMETHING SWEET

May the God of hope fill you with all joy and peace as you trust in Him,
so that you may overflow with hope by the power of the Holy Spirit.

– ROMANS 15:13

Here's what I want to accomplish in the next _____ weeks, with God's help:

_____

_____

_____

_____

_____

_____

_____

_____

_____

_____

_____

_____

_____

_____

_____

_____

_____

_____

_____

_____

_____

"If we truly have faith in God, if we truly lean our entire personality on Him in absolute trust and confidence in His power, wisdom and goodness, we will not be anxious or worried."

– JOYCE (SEE COLOSSIANS 1:4)

WHAT GETS YOU EXCITED?

So then, there is still awaiting a full and complete Sabbath-rest reserved for the [true] people of God; For he who has once entered [God's] rest also has ceased from [the weariness and pain] of human labors, just as God rested from those labors peculiarly His own. Let us therefore be zealous and exert ourselves and strive diligently to enter that rest [of God, to know and experience it for ourselves], that no one may fall or perish by the same kind of unbelief and disobedience [into which those in the wilderness fell]. – HEBREWS 4:9-11

PROCRASTINATION

These are the things or habits that cause me to lose track of time.

WHAT INSPIRES YOU?

Come to Me, all you who labor and are heavy-laden and overburdened, and I will cause you to rest. [I will ease and relieve and refresh your souls.] Take My yoke upon you and learn of Me, for I am gentle (meek) and humble (lowly) in heart, and you will find rest (relief and ease and refreshment and recreation and blessed quiet) for your souls. – MATTHEW 11:28-29

What would you do if you had the time, money and resources to do it?

Draw out a recent dream.

And the peace of God, which transcends all understanding, will guard your hearts and minds in Christ Jesus. - **PHILIPPIANS 4:7**

The BEST advice I've ever received about worrying was:

The WORST advice someone ever gave me was:

Here's what I learned from it: _____

_____

_____

_____

_____

_____

_____

_____

_____

_____

_____

_____

_____

_____

_____

_____

_____

_____

_____

_____

_____

_____

"Every one of us goes through seasons when things don't work out the way we would like. But Jesus, our Prince of Peace, has overcome the world." – JOYCE

REMEMBER TO

THANK GOD

IN EVERY CIRCUMSTANCE,

EVERY DAY

(1 Thessalonians 5:18)

WHAT MAKES YOU HAPPY?

A happy heart is good medicine and a cheerful mind works healing, but a broken spirit dries up the bones. — PROVERBS 17:22

Good things can come from challenges. Think about the challenges of the last year. Write about the good things you've learned about yourself and about God.

In God's Hands

Trace your hands and decorate them.

For You have been my help, and in the shadow of Your wings will I rejoice.

— PSALM 63:7

LETTER TO GOD

Write a prayer letter to God, beginning with what you are
thankful for. Then let Him know what you need. Then look
back on this prayer from time to time to see how He answers it.

Dear God,

Thank you for... _____

_____

_____

_____

_____

_____

_____

_____

_____

_____

_____

_____

_____

_____

_____

Devote yourselves to prayer, being watchful and thankful.

— COLOSSIANS 4:2

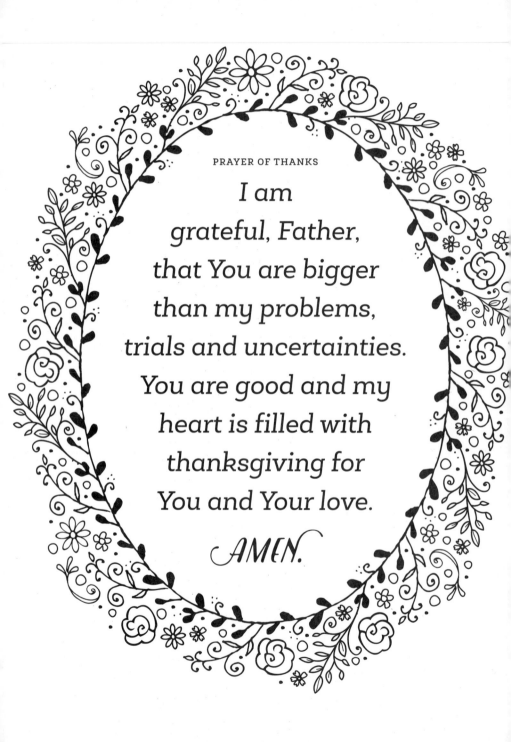

PRAYER OF THANKS

I am
grateful, Father,
that You are bigger
than my problems,
trials and uncertainties.
You are good and my
heart is filled with
thanksgiving for
You and Your love.
AMEN.

DRAW ANYTHING AT ALL...

For You have been my help, and in the shadow of Your wings will I rejoice.

— PSALM 63:7

Today I'm thankful for:

_____
_____
_____
_____
_____
_____
_____
_____
_____
_____
_____
_____
_____
_____
_____
_____
_____
_____
_____
_____
_____
_____

"Positive, thankful thoughts don't happen by accident;
you can choose to practice them. And remember, practice
makes perfect." – JOYCE

My Favorite Things

Draw what you love the most.

Your problems are no match for God. List
the ways that God helps you overcome
your problems:

Casting the whole of your care [all your anxieties, all your worries, all your concerns, once and for all] on Him, for He cares for you affectionately and cares about you watchfully. — 1 PETER 5:7

List the people in your life you are grateful for, starting from when you were a child until now:

_____

I'm expecting God to...

Lean on, trust in, and be confident in the Lord with all your heart and mind and do not rely on your own insight or understanding. In all your ways know, recognize and acknowledge Him, and He will direct and make straight and plain your paths. — PROVERBS 3:5-6

$\mathcal{S}$TART DOING...

Good habits I want to set

1. _____

2. _____

3. _____

4. _____

5. _____

6. _____

7. _____

8. _____

9. _____

10. _____

STOP DOING...

Bad habits I want to break

1. _____

2. _____

3. _____

4. _____

5. _____

6. _____

7. _____

8. _____

9. _____

10. _____

If you were certain you would NOT fail, write about everything you would attempt to do.

_____

_____

_____

_____

_____

_____

_____

_____

_____

_____

_____

_____

_____

_____

_____

_____

_____

_____

_____

_____

_____

_____

I will say of the Lord, "He is my refuge and my fortress, my God, in whom I trust. – PSALM 91:2

VISIONARY

Ask God to reveal your future in Him — what do you hope for?

"Whoever you are, wherever you are, whatever you've been through, it's never too late to begin again." - JOYCE

What did God teach you from the last thing you failed...

About yourself: _____

_____

_____

_____

_____

_____

_____

_____

_____

_____

_____

_____

_____

_____

_____

_____

_____

_____

_____

_____

_____

_____

About others:

_____

_____

_____

_____

_____

_____

_____

_____

_____

_____

_____

About God:

_____

_____

_____

_____

_____

_____

_____

_____

_____

_____

"Never, never, never, never give up!" – WINSTON CHURCHILL

My Best

List things you like about yourself.

Pick three people to pray for, and then write your prayers here. Check back from time to time to observe how God answered your prayers.

Person #1: _____

_____

_____

_____

_____

_____

_____

_____

_____

_____

_____

_____

_____

_____

_____

_____

_____

_____

_____

_____

_____

_____

_____

_____

_____

_____

_____

_____

_____

_____

_____

_____

_____

_____

_____

_____

_____

_____

_____

_____

_____

_____

_____

"When you turn the construction of your life over to God, He builds something beautiful." – JOYCE

Person #2: _____

Person #3: _____

ILLUSTRATED QUOTES BY ME

Write down your own words of wisdom.

Let us then fearlessly and confidently and boldly draw near to the throne of grace (the throne of God's unmerited favor to us sinners), that we may receive mercy [for our failures] and find grace to help in good time for every need [appropriate help and well-timed help, coming just when we need it].

— HEBREWS 4:16

List every good thing that has happened over the last six months. Then thank God for them.

WHEN YOU

LIVE FOR

& OBEY

GOD,

HE CAUSES EVERYONE
– EVEN YOUR ENEMIES –

TO BE AT

PEACE

WITH YOU

(Proverbs 16:7)

You are fearfully and wonderfully made!
(See PSALM 139:14.) What do you see when you look
in the mirror? Write about your reflection.

Write a list of God-given qualities that define your personality.

_____   _____

_____   _____

_____   _____

_____   _____

_____   _____

_____   _____

_____   _____

_____   _____

_____   _____

_____   _____

_____   _____

_____   _____

_____   _____

_____   _____

_____   _____

_____   _____

What forces you out of your comfort zone? How did you react the last time it happened?

Yet amid all these things we are more than conquerors and gain a
surpassing victory through Him Who loved us. — ROMANS 8:37

Things I've Done That I'm Proud Of

JUST DOODLE...

"Simple, childlike faith pleases God. He already knows we are not perfect and will not behave perfectly all the time." – JOYCE

WHERE HAVE YOU TRAVELED?

List all the new places you would like to visit
if you had the time and resources to travel.

We can come to God without fear because we have put our trust in Christ. — EPHESIANS 3:12

REFLECTION

Draw or paste a picture of yourself.

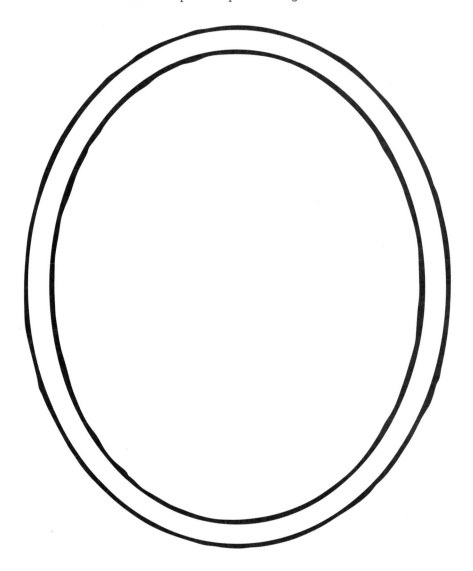

WHAT DOES GOD SEE IN YOU?

"To live a life you enjoy, you will need confidence that comes from knowing you are right with God through Jesus, a healthy, positive self-image, and good relationships with others." - JOYCE

Write about the last time you did something you were afraid to try. How did you feel afterward?

_____

_____

_____

_____

_____

_____

_____

_____

_____

_____

_____

_____

_____

_____

_____

_____

_____

_____

_____

_____

_____

_____

"We need to give God our reputation and let Him be in charge of it from now on. After all, He can do anything, and He is for us!" – JOYCE

DRAW YOUR FAVORITE PLACE

For I know the thoughts and plans that I have for you, says the Lord, thoughts and plans for welfare and peace and not for evil, to give you hope in your final outcome. — JEREMIAH 29:11

I AM...

List all the great things that represent you:

LOVED BY GOD

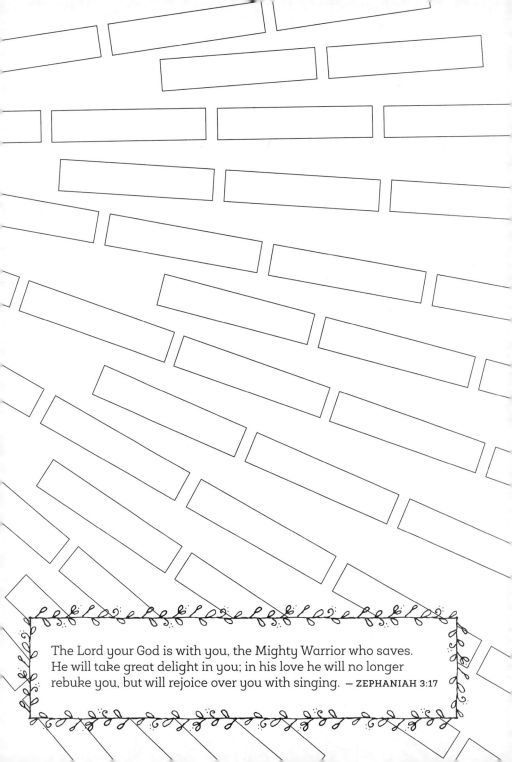

The Lord your God is with you, the Mighty Warrior who saves. He will take great delight in you; in his love he will no longer rebuke you, but will rejoice over you with singing. — ZEPHANIAH 3:17

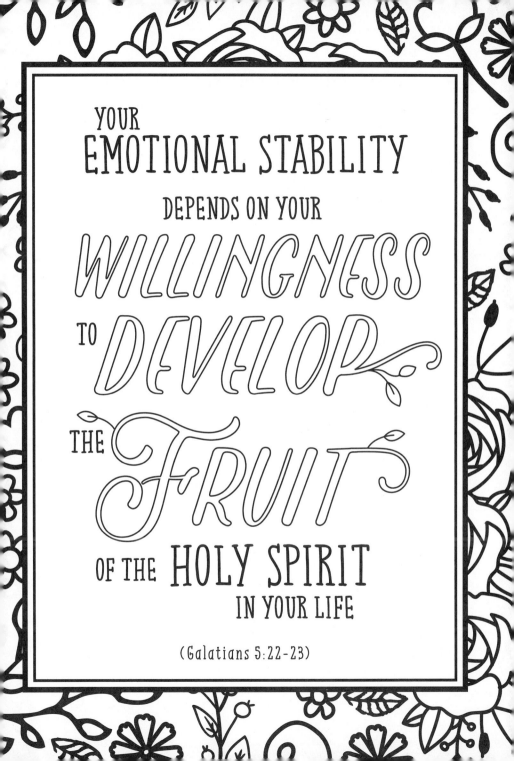

YOUR
EMOTIONAL STABILITY
DEPENDS ON YOUR
WILLINGNESS
TO *DEVELOP*
THE *FRUIT*
OF THE HOLY SPIRIT
IN YOUR LIFE

(Galatians 5:22-23)

Think about a recent challenge. How did you react to it emotionally? How would you react differently if you had the experience again?

What is emotional intelligence? Look it up if you don't know. Do you think it's important and why?

For God did not give us a spirit of timidity (of cowardice, of craven and cringing and fawning fear), but [He has given us a spirit] of power and of love and of calm and well-balanced mind and discipline and self-control. —2 TIMOTHY 1:7

List everthing you like to do just to have fun.

_____

_____

_____

_____

_____

_____

_____

_____

_____

_____

_____

_____

_____

_____

_____

_____

_____

_____

_____

_____

_____

_____

"Wise choices have nothing to do with feelings. You can feel wrong and still do what is right." – JOYCE

Top Fears

List or draw your top fears. What will you do to overcome them?

Therefore my heart is glad and my glory [my inner self] rejoices;
my body too shall rest and confidently dwell in safety. — PSALM 16:9

If I had no access to television or social media for one month, I would be able to...

ABOUT ME

This is what I'm doing right now:

WEARING _____

WANTING _____

NEEDING _____

THINKING _____

LOVING _____

LISTENING _____

PRAYING _____

JUST DOODLE...

You are my hiding place; you will protect me from trouble and surround me with songs of deliverance. — PSALM32:7

I would like to be remembered for...

DRAW HOW YOU'RE FEELING

"Life isn't fair, but God is. We may not know why things happen the way they do, but we can know God." - JOYCE

My habits that I would like God to help me change are...

Casting the whole of your care [all your anxieties, all your worries, all your concerns, once and for all] on Him, for He cares for you affectionately and cares about you watchfully. — 1 PETER 5:7

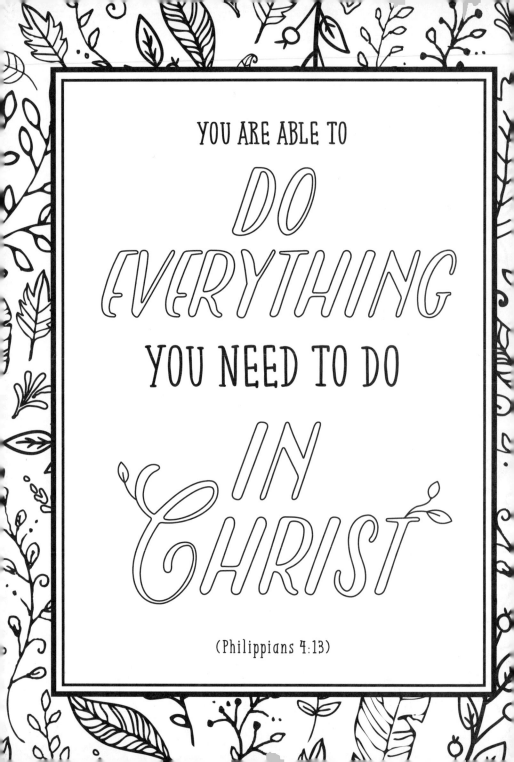

DRAW THINGS THAT START WITH THE SAME LETTER AS YOUR NAME

Who are your greatest encouragers and examples of encouragement, and why?

DRAW A TREE

Fill your tree with major life events & accomplishments. Come back with new ones as they happen, and see how full your tree becomes.

I am the Vine; you are the branches. Whoever lives in Me and I in him bears much (abundant) fruit. However, apart from Me [cut off from vital union with Me] you can do nothing. — JOHN 15:5

Write about the last time you had to stand your
ground. What did that experience teach you?

_____

_____

_____

_____

_____

_____

_____

_____

_____

_____

_____

_____

_____

_____

_____

_____

_____

_____

_____

_____

_____

For he will command his angels concerning you to guard you in all your ways; they will lift you up in their hands, so that you will not strike your foot against a stone. — PSALM 91:11-12

CREATE AN ART PIECE ONLY USING TRIANGLES

"Courage is not the absence of fear; it is action in the presence of fear. Bold people do what they know they should do – not what they feel like doing."

Write about being fearless. Do you see yourself as courageous? Why or why not?

_____

_____

_____

_____

_____

_____

_____

_____

_____

_____

_____

_____

_____

_____

_____

_____

_____

_____

_____

_____

_____

_____

_____

"God uses men and women who are set on obeying and pleasing Him, not those who are controlled by the fear of man." - JOYCE

CREATE A COLLAGE THAT MAKES YOU LAUGH

"Love is the healing balm that the world needs, and God offers it freely and continuously." - JOYCE

For we [Christians] are the true circumcision, who worship God in spirit and by the Spirit of God and exult and glory and pride ourselves in Jesus Christ, and put no confidence or dependence [on what we are] in the flesh and on outward privileges and physical advantages and external appearances.

— PHILIPPIANS 3:3

Write about some of the best constructive criticism you have received. Did it prompt you to change anything?

Think about something you want to accomplish. Would you still do it if you were not going to receive the credit? Why or why not?

What do you want out of life? What desires has God planted deep in your heart?

_____

_____

_____

_____

_____

_____

_____

_____

_____

_____

_____

_____

_____

_____

_____

_____

_____

_____

_____

_____

And I will make of you a great nation, and I will bless you [with abundant increase of favors] and make your name famous and distinguished, and you will be a blessing [dispensing good to others]. — GENESIS 12:2

But let endurance and steadfastness and patience have full play and do a thorough work, so that you may be [people] perfectly and fully developed [with no defects], lacking in nothing. — JAMES 1:4

Daily Priorities

Make a list of what's truly important to you and use
that list to help you in your daily decision making.

The Lord is my shepherd, I lack nothing. He makes me lie down
in green pastures, he leads me beside quiet waters, he refreshes
my soul. He guides me along the right paths for his name's sake.

—PSALM 23:1-3

Sunday:

Monday:

Tuesday:

Wednesday:

Thursday:

Friday:

Saturday:

LONG-TERM PERSONAL GOALS

And the actions I will take to meet my goals.

Goal #1: _____

Actions I will take: _____

_____

_____

_____

Goal #2: _____

Actions I will take: _____

_____

_____

_____

Goal #3: _____

Actions I will take: _____

_____

_____

_____

$\mathcal{S}$HORT-TERM PERSONAL GOALS

And the actions I will take to meet my goals.

Goal #1: _____

Actions I will take: _____

_____

_____

_____

Goal #2: _____

Actions I will take: _____

_____

_____

_____

Goal #3: _____

Actions I will take: _____

_____

_____

_____

THINGS YOU WANT IN LIFE

》》》 … ♡ … 《《《

"God never asks us to do anything that
won't eventually make our lives better."

Write about what it means to be "authentic."

Lean on, trust in, and be confident in the Lord with all your heart
and mind and do not rely on your own insight or understanding.

— PROVERBS 3:5

DRAW SOMETHING YOU COULDN'T LIVE WITHOUT

Little children, keep yourselves from idols (false gods) — [from anything and everything that would occupy the place in your heart due to God, from any sort of substitute for Him that would take first place in your life]. Amen (so let it be). - 1 JOHN 5:21

MAPPING YOUR GOALS

Get in the habit of creating a schedule based on goals you want to reach. Then stick to it. Start here with a goal, and mapping how to get to your goal before starting another goal.

Goals:

Things to do this month:

Things to do this week:

Things to do today:

Bucket List (save these ideas for later):

Reflect on the goodness around you that is easily overlooked and taken for granted.

_____

_____

_____

_____

_____

_____

_____

_____

_____

_____

_____

_____

_____

_____

_____

The Lord is my Shepherd [to feed, guide, and shield me], I shall not lack. He makes me lie down in [fresh, tender] green pastures; He leads me beside the still and restful waters. He refreshes and restores my life (my self); He leads me in the paths of righteousness [uprightness and right standing with Him—not for my earning it, but] for His name's sake. — PSALM 23:1-3

CREATE YOUR OWN
DOODLE PATTERN

TRUST GOD

EVEN WHEN

THINGS

DON'T MAKE SENSE TO YOU

(Proverbs 3:5)